This Book Belongs to

Marie R.

CHILDREN'S CHOICE®

Timothy Goes to School

The Dial Press

NEW YORK

TIMOTHY GOES TO SCHOOL

Story and pictures by
Rosemary Wells

For Jennifer and Karen H.

Published by The Dial Press
1 Dag Hammarskjold Plaza
New York, New York 10017

 A Children's Choice® Book Club Edition From Scholastic Book Services

Timothy's mother made him a brand-new sunsuit for the first day of school.

"Hooray!" said Timothy.

Timothy went to school in his new sunsuit with his new book
and his new pencil.

"Good morning!" said Timothy.

"Good morning!" said the teacher.

"Timothy," said the teacher, "this is Claude.

Claude, this is Timothy. I'm sure you'll be the best of friends."

"Hello!" said Timothy.

"Nobody wears a sunsuit on the first day of school," said Claude.

During playtime Timothy hoped and hoped that
Claude would fall into a puddle.

But he didn't.

When Timothy came home, his mother asked, "How was school today?"

"Nobody wears a sunsuit on the first day of school," said Timothy.

"I will make you a beautiful new jacket," said Timothy's mother.

Timothy wore his new jacket the next day.

"Hello!" said Timothy to Claude.
"You're not supposed to wear party clothes
on the second day of school," said Claude.

All day Timothy wanted and wanted Claude to make a mistake.

But he didn't.

When Timothy went home, his mother asked, "How did it go?"

"You're not supposed to wear party clothes on the second day of
   school," said Timothy.
"Don't worry," said Timothy's mother. "Tomorrow you just wear
   something in-between like everyone else."

The next day Timothy went to school in his favorite shirt.

"Look!" said Timothy. "You are wearing the same shirt I am!"

"No," said Claude, "you are wearing the same shirt that *I* am."

During lunch Timothy wished and wished that Claude
would have to eat all alone.

But he didn't.

After school Timothy's mother could not find Timothy. "Where are you?" she called.

"I'm never going back to school," said Timothy.

"Why not?" called his mother.

"Because Claude is the smartest and the best at everything and he has all the friends," said Timothy.

"You'll feel better in your new football shirt," said Timothy's mother.

Timothy did not feel better in his new football shirt.

That morning Claude played the saxophone.

"I can't stand it anymore," said a voice next to Timothy.

It was Violet.

"You can't stand what?" Timothy asked Violet.

"Grace!" said Violet. "She sings. She dances. She counts up to a
thousand and she sits next to me!"

During playtime Timothy and Violet stayed together.

Violet said, "I can't believe you've been here all along!"
"Will you come home and have cookies with me after school?"
Timothy asked.

On the way home Timothy and Violet laughed so much about
Claude and Grace that they both got the hiccups.

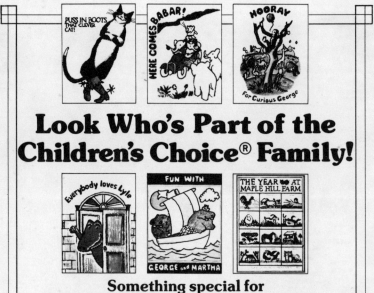

Look Who's Part of the Children's Choice® Family!

Something special for Children's Choice® Book Club members

You can get all these storybook favorites—Puss in Boots, Babar, Curious George, Lyle, George and Martha and The Year at Maple Hill Farm—to hang up on your wall. They're big (17" × 22") and beautiful posters, printed in full color on high quality paper. Best of all, you can get all 6 for just $3.95, including postage and handling.

To order your set of 6 Children's Choice® posters, please send your name, address and $3.95 in check or money order to:

**CHILDREN'S CHOICE® POSTERS
2931 East McCarty St.
P.O. Box 1068
Jefferson City, Mo. 65102**

Please allow 3-6 weeks for delivery. Your posters are mailed in a tube, so they won't be creased at all.